:thelwell's.
RIDING ACADEMY

FOR
DAVID

thelwell's

RIDING ACADEMY

EYRE METHUEN

FIRST PUBLISHED IN 1965
BY METHUEN AND CO LTD
11 NEW FETTER LANE, LONDON EC4
COPYRIGHT © 1963, 1964 BY NORMAN THELWELL
AND BEAVERBROOK NEWSPAPERS LTD
FIRST PUBLISHED IN THIS EDITION 1969
REPRINTED TWICE 1970, 1971 AND 1972
PRINTED IN GREAT BRITAIN BY
T. AND A. CONSTABLE LTD., EDINBURGH

SBN 413 29560 5

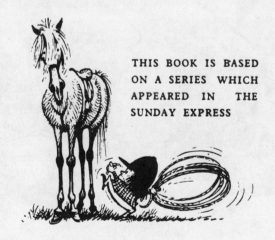

THIS BOOK IS BASED
ON A SERIES WHICH
APPEARED IN THE
SUNDAY EXPRESS

CONTENTS

" REMEMBER WHAT I TOLD YOU GIRLS,
NEVER LET HIM SEE YOU'RE AFRAID. "

THE MOUNT

" DO YOU HAVE ONE LIKE THIS IN DAPPLE GREY ? "

SOME CHILDREN DISCOVER THE JOYS OF
RIDING AT A VERY EARLY AGE . . . . . .

... OTHERS PREFER TO WAIT UNTIL THEY ARE BIGGER.

ONCE IN THE SADDLE, HOWEVER, THEY
ARE ALL RELUCTANT TO LEAVE IT.

FINDING A RELIABLE PONY IS NOT EASY —

PROFESSIONAL ADVICE SHOULD BE SOUGHT...

FINDING A RELIABLE PROFESSIONAL
CAN ALSO HAVE ITS SNAGS.

YOU MUST BEAR IN MIND
THAT FAT PONIES CAN BE
HARD ON THE LEGS....

AND THIN ONES HARD ON THE JODHPURS

YOUNG ANIMALS CAN BE UNPREDICTABLE

AND OLD ONES JUST THE REVERSE

BUT **NEVER** BUY THE FIRST CNE YOU SEE . . . . .

.... SOME DAY YOU MAY WANT TO SELL HIM.

IF YOU BUY A PONY THAT IS DIFFICULT TO CATCH —

       TAKE PLENTY OF LUMP SUGAR WITH YOU

AND EAT AS MUCH OF IT AS YOU CAN . . . . .

YOU WILL NEED ALL THE ENERGY YOU CAN GET.

YOU MAY LEARN A GREAT DEAL
ABOUT A PONY BY LOOKING
AT HIS TEETH

THIS OFTEN APPLIES ALSO . . . . .

.... TO THE RIDER.

FIRST PRINCIPLES

" NO! NO! DEIRDRE, YOU'VE GOT THE WRONG
FOOT IN THAT STIRRUP."

MOST CHILDREN MAKE VERY RAPID STRIDES AS SOON
AS THEY GET INTO THE SADDLE

ALTHOUGH STEADY PROGRESS IS LESS EASY TO MAINTAIN —

MUTUAL RESPECT MUST BE ESTABLISHED
                    BETWEEN PONY AND RIDER

NEVER SPEAK ANGRILY TO YOUR PONY

USE A KIND, GENTLE VOICE

IT WILL BE JUST AS EFFECTIVE

NEVER USE SPURS —

DO NOT EXPECT HIM TO BE ABLE TO READ YOUR MIND

SHOW HIM EXACTLY WHAT YOU WOULD LIKE HIM TO DO....

HE'LL BE VERY HAPPY TO OBLIGE YOU.

PONIES ARE WELL KNOWN FOR THEIR COURAGE

BUT THEY CAN BE SHY, SENSITIVE CREATURES ....

SO IF ANY OBSTACLE SHOULD CAUSE HIM TROUBLE...

. . .TAKE HIM BACK . . .

. . . . REASSURE HIM . . . .

. . . AND MAKE HIM DO IT AGAIN

THE ACADEMY

" HAND UP THE ONE WHO SPOTTED MY DELIBERATE MISTAKE "

ALWAYS GET UP EARLY WHEN GOING TO RIDING SCHOOL —

YOU'LL NEED PLENTY OF TIME . . . .

.... TO WAKEN YOUR PONY

DON'T DAWDLE ON THE WAY ...

DON'T TRY TO BE CLEVER ....

ALWAYS ENTER A RIDING SCHOOL BY THE FRONT GATE

MAKE FRIENDS WITH THE OTHER CHILDREN

YOU WILL LEARN A LOT FROM THEM

JUST SITTING ON A PONY'S BACK IS NOT RIDING —

SO WORK HARD AT YOUR STUDIES...

THERE WILL BE PLENTY OF TIME FOR PLAY

MOST INSTRUCTORS ENJOY A JOKE . . . .

BUT DON'T GO TOO FAR ——

EXPULSIONS ARE DIFFICULT FOR ALL CONCERNED

CARE OF YOUR PONY

" DON'T JUST SIT THERE, DEAR - HURRY HOME
BEFORE HE CATCHES A CHILL."

IT IS UNKIND TO RIDE YOUR PONY TOO FAST -

INSUFFICIENT EXERCISE, HOWEVER,
CAN LEAD TO EXCESSIVE FAT ..

SO GIVE HIM A GOOD LIVELY TROT EVERY DAY

THE RESULT WILL ASTONISH YOU.

NEGLECTING YOUR PONY'S COAT
IS A SERIOUS MATTER ...

... WHICH CANNOT FAIL ...

... TO CAUSE TROUBLE

IF FLIES BOTHER HIM IN HOT WEATHER . . . . . .

TIE A SPRIG OF ELDER TO HIS BROW BAND . . .

HE WILL FIND IT A GREAT RELIEF

YOUR PONY'S SHOES SHOULD BE CHECKED REGULARLY

NEGLECT OF THIS SIMPLE PRECAUTION..

CAN LEAD TO SORE FEET.

YOU MUST LEARN TO RECOGNISE SIGNS
THAT YOUR PONY IS OFF COLOUR —

ROARING MAY INDICATE WIND TROUBLES . . .

... AND KICKING MAY MEAN A SORE SPOT . . . . .

YOU WILL KNOW WHEN IT'S TIME
TO CALL FOR THE VET

SAFETY PRECAUTIONS

" WHAT HAVE YOU DONE WITH HER THIS TIME ? "

MAKE SURE YOU KNOW HOW TO PICK UP HIS FOOT . . .

LACK OF ABILITY IN THIS DIRECTION

MAY CAUSE YOU INCONVENIENCE

NEVER SHOUT 'GEE UP'

..... WHEN TEACHER IS MOUNTING

ALWAYS EXAMINE FENCES CAREFULLY
BEFORE JUMPING

THIS WILL ENABLE YOU TO BE READY . . .

FOR ANY EMERGENCY

NEVER TRY OUT NOVEL WAYS OF

GETTING INTO THE SADDLE

YOU'LL ENJOY QUITE ENOUGH VARIETY —

— GETTING OUT OF IT

IF ACCIDENTS ARE LIKELY TO OCCUR ...

... AVOID WORRY ...

... BY MAKING SURE THAT THERE IS A QUALIFIED VET
IN ATTENDANCE

REMEMBER THAT THE RULES OF THE ROAD
APPLY TO YOU...

AS WELL AS TO OTHER ROAD USERS

ALL ROAD SIGNS MUST
BE STRICTLY OBEYED

AND ALL HAND SIGNALS
CORRECTLY GIVEN.

SOME RIDERS LIKE TO HAVE A LOT OF
BANDAGES ON THEIR HORSES

THIS IS NOT ALWAYS AS POINTLESS....

. . . AS IT MAY APPEAR.

WHAT TO WEAR

" I'M BREAKING IN A NEW PAIR OF BOOTS "

A SMART TURNOUT IS
EXTREMELY IMPORTANT....

A RIDER'S ABILITY CAN USUALLY BE JUDGED

FROM HER APPEARANCE

THERE IS NO POINT IN BEING WELL
GROOMED YOURSELF, HOWEVER,

UNLESS YOU ARE PREPARED TO MAKE YOUR PONY...

... LOOK THE SAME

ROOMY JODHPURS ARE ADVISABLE...

AND A HARD HAT IS A MUST ..

ELABORATE WHIPS IMPRESS NOBODY —
BUT REMEMBER . . .

THE MOST ESSENTIAL ITEM

IN A RIDER'S WARDROBE

IS A GOOD PAIR OF BOOTS.

GOOD MANNERS

" DON'T BE SO MEAN, GEORGINA -
LET CHRISTABEL HAVE A TURN "

NEVER LET YOUR PONY NIP OTHER PEOPLES' . . . . .

IT IS BAD MANNERS FOR ONE THING....

AND CAN LEAD TO PAINFUL RESULTS

THE JUDGE'S DECISION MUST ALWAYS BE
ACCEPTED AS FINAL

DO NOT BLAME YOUR INSTRUCTOR . . . . .

... EVERYTIME SOMETHING GOES WRONG

DON'T PLAY WITH YOUR PONY IN THE GARDEN —

OR ALLOW HIM INTO THE HOUSE

DON'T MAKE FUN OF OTHER PEOPLE . . . .

... YOU MAY NOT BE PERFECT YOURSELF

YOU MUST NOT EXPECT YOUR MOTHER
TO KEEP YOUR PONY CLEAN

OR YOUR FATHER TO GIVE HIM EXERCISE

NEVER FORGET THAT WINNING PRIZES
IS NOT EVERYTHING . . . .

THOSE WHO MAKE THE ODD BLUNDER . . . .

ARE OFTEN MORE POPULAR.

ACADEMY PICTURES

" YOU HAVE TO APPROACH HER SLOWLY AND QUIETLY . . . .

... HOLDING OUT A LOLLIPOP. "

" IT'S JUST A QUESTION OF WHICH SHE BREAKS FIRST.

THE PONY OR HER NECK."

" YOU'RE WASTING YOUR TIME DARLINGS —

YOU CAN LEAD THEM TO THE WATER . . .

... BUT YOU **CAN'T** MAKE THEM DRINK. "

" PUTTING SHOES ON FOR YOU LOT IS PLAYING

OLD HARRY WITH MY EYESIGHT "

" NEXT YEAR YOU CAN GO PONY TREKKING ON YOUR OWN"

" THEY KNOW PERFECTLY WELL THEY'RE SUPPOSED
TO DRINK LEMONADE AS A STIRRUP CUP. "

" THAT WAS MEAN — TELLING HER YOU'RE

ENGAGED TO DAVID BROOM. "

" HE CAN MANAGE ON TINNED FOOD . WHY CAN'T YOU? "

"IF I LAY MY HANDS ON THOSE PERISHING KIDS".....

"HOW MANY TRADING STAMPS DID
THEY GIVE YOU WITH HIM?"

" I WISH YOU WOULDN'T KEEP HIDING THEM IN
YOUR BEDROOM. WE'LL HAVE THE WHOLE HOUSE
OVERRUN WITH HOUNDS AGAIN."

" I'M SORRY MRS. CHADWICK
BUT WHEN YOUR DAUGHTER FELL
AT THE DOUBLE OXER,
I'M AFRAID SHE BROKE A LEG."